STARTING OVER

NORTH POINT
RESOURCES

STARTING OVER

Study Guide

Here are some ideas to get you started.

LEADERS:

Need some help? It's okay. We all do.
A full walk-through of the study guide with notes on how to navigate each session is available at **groupleaders.org/startingover.**

VIDEOS:

The video sessions that complement this study can be found on the:

- **Anthology Mobile App** (free on the iTunes App Store and Google Play)
- **Starting Over DVD** (available on Amazon)

POST A
PICTURE OF
YOUR GROUP USING
#StartingOverSeries.

Your next study could be on us!

1. HANG OUT.
(about 30 minutes)

Our life moves so fast these days. Take some time to talk about what's going on in the life of those in your group. Asking about things like job interviews, the health of their kids, and how their weeks are going goes a long way in building community.

2. WATCH THE VIDEO AND DOODLE ALONG.
(about 20 minutes)

When we designed this study guide, we had note-taking in mind. So while you're watching the video, take advantage of the extra space and grid pages for notes and/or drawings, depending on your note-taking style.

3. DISCUSS AND COMPLETE THE ACTIVITIES
(about 45 minutes)

Depending on the session, your group will have Discussion Questions and scenarios to think through, as well as activities to do. Putting pen to paper can give you deeper insight into the content.

4. PRAYER
(about 5 minutes)

Keep this simple and real. Use the Bottom Line as your prayer, asking God to help you make it happen that week.

Video Notes

PART 1
Three Myths

VIDEO RECAP

STARTING OVER: HOW TO ENSURE NEXT TIME WON'T BE LIKE LAST TIME.

We learn from our mistakes in the areas that matter least.

We repeat our mistakes in the areas that matter most.

WHEN WE'RE FACED WITH STARTING OVER, THREE MYTHS CAUSE US TO REPEAT OUR MISTAKES:

1. *Myth:* Experience makes me wiser.
   Truth: Evaluated experience makes you wiser.

2. *Myth*: Since I know better, I'll do better.
   Truth: Know better ≠ Ability to do better.

3. *Myth:* Time is against me.
   Truth: Time is your friend.

"STARTING OVER" STORIES IN THE BIBLE:

- _____ killed an Egyptian and returned to Egypt 40 years later to free Israel from slavery (Exodus 2–12)

- David went from shepherd boy to king. (1 Samuel 16)
- The apostle _____ went from persecutor of Christians to church planter. (Acts 9)

WHAT DO THEY HAVE IN COMMON?

Each person returned with divine _____
and an abiding _____.

* *Destiny:* I know God has something for me. He will redeem my past—the pain and my failures.

* *Humility:* I have confidence in God rather than in myself.

CONCLUSION:

You can't rush a start-over. Remember that time is your friend. And if you allow him, God will redeem the failure of last time, and next time will be better.

Answer Key for Blanks	
Moses	destiny
Paul	humility

Notes

LET'S TALK ABOUT IT

1 Did you hear anything in the video that really stood out to you or that you may even disagree with?

2 In the scenarios below, which of the myths that Andy mentioned is at play, and how might you respond to a friend dealing with that situation?

- *Experience Myth:* Experience makes me wiser.
- *Knowledge Myth:* Since I know better, I'll do better.
- *Time Myth:* Time is against me.

SCENARIO #1

A friend's divorce was finalized about a month ago. She tells you she met someone she's interested in, but she isn't sure she should begin dating again.

SCENARIO #2

You have a close friend who has struggled with alcoholism but has been sober for almost five years. He says he's stopped attending Alcoholics Anonymous meetings because he knows what he needs to do to stay sober.

SCENARIO #3

A friend lost a significant amount of money in an investment deal. He tells you about a risky new investment option that he thinks may help him make back the money he lost.

3 Does the idea of "redeeming" a piece of your past (making good come from it) give you hope, or would you rather leave it in your past? Explain.

4 Romans 8:28 reads: *And we know that in all things God works for the good of those who love him.*

Explain how this verse makes you feel. Is it helpful to you? Is it difficult for you to believe?

5 Have you seen God use something painful in someone you know and turn it into something good?

THIS WEEK, THINK ABOUT...

In what area of your life do you hope *next time* is different than *last time?*

How do you need God to help you?

PRAYER

God, help me know how to plan for my next time to be better than my last time.

STARTING OVER:
how to ensure
NEXT TIME
won't be like
LAST TIME.

POST A
PICTURE OF
YOUR GROUP USING
#StartingOverSeries.

Your next study could be on us!

Video Notes

PART 2
Own It

VIDEO RECAP

INTRODUCTION

One reason history repeats itself in our lives is that we don't own our parts in those histories. Instead, we convince ourselves there is nothing for us to own. We decide it was all the other person's fault.

When something important ends, you have to look back in order to move ahead.

WE ARE NATURAL-BORN _____.

> *Then the man and his wife heard the sound of the Lord God as he was walking in the garden in the cool of the day, and they hid from the Lord God among the trees of the garden. But the Lord God called to the man, "Where are you?" He answered, "I heard you in the garden, and I was afraid because I was naked; so I hid." And he said, "Who told you that you were naked? Have you eaten from the tree that I commanded you not to eat from?" The man said, "The woman you put here with me—she gave me some fruit from the tree, and I ate it." Then the Lord God said to the woman, "What is this you have done?" The woman said, "The serpent deceived me, and I ate."*

> *(Genesis 3:8–13)*

After disobeying God, Adam and Eve didn't own it. They hid.

Adam blamed Eve and God.

Eve blamed the serpent.

YOU CAN'T BLAME _____ INTO A BETTER _____. (MATTHEW 5:8)

Blame enables us to smuggle our issues into our futures.

Blame sets us up for a repeat performance.

Blessed are the pure in heart, for they will see God. (Matthew 5:8)

CONCLUSION

If you want to take all of you into the future, you have to come out of hiding. And even though coming out of hiding can be painful and shameful, it's also beneficial.

You make peace with your past by owning your piece of the past.

POST A PICTURE OF YOUR GROUP USING #StartingOverSeries.

Your next study could be on us!

Answer Key for Blanks

blamers	future
your way	

Notes

LET'S TALK ABOUT IT

1 What are some excuses people use to blame others when something goes wrong? Think about what you might tell your boss or what your child says when he or she is caught.

2 Read Genesis 3:8–13 and answer the question that follows the verse.

Then the man and his wife heard the sound of the Lord God as he was walking in the garden in the cool of the day, and they hid from the Lord God among the trees of the garden. But the Lord God called to the man, "Where are you?" [The man] answered, "I heard you in the garden, and I was afraid because I was naked; so I hid." And [God] said, "Who told you that you were naked? Have you eaten from the tree that I commanded you not to eat from?" The man said, "The woman you put here with me—she gave me some fruit from the tree, and I ate it." Then the Lord God said to the woman, "What is this you have done?" The woman said, "The serpent deceived me, and I ate."

Why do you think failure makes people hide or blame others instead of owning it?

3 Think about a time when a choice someone else made caused you to suffer a setback. What did it cost you? How did you respond?

4 Take a few minutes to complete the following activity individually and then continue the conversation.

    A. Identify an area of your life in which you hope next time will be different than last time. Write it in the margin.

    B. Using the circle, draw a slice or wedge that represents the percentage of the situation you are willing to own. (It could be the entire circle, 50, 25, or even 2 percent.)

    C. In the margin, write some details about what's in your slice of the pie—some pieces of the situation you are willing to own.

5 If you feel comfortable sharing, walk the group through your answers to the previous activity.

THIS WEEK, THINK ABOUT...

If the other person refuses to own his or her part, do you think it's possible to own your part of the past? Why or why not?

PRAYER

God, help me make peace with my past. Help me realize the parts of my past that I need to own.

YOU MAKE
peace
WITH YOUR PAST BY
owning your
PIECE OF THE
past.

Video Notes

PART 3
Rethink It

VIDEO RECAP

THINKING YOUR WAY TO A BETTER FUTURE

Therefore, I urge you in view of God's mercy to offer your bodies as a living sacrifice, holy and pleasing to God—this is your true and proper worship. Do not conform to the pattern of this world, but be transformed by the renewing of your mind.

(Romans 12:1–2)

Renew = Restore

CONFORMED VS. _____

- Conformed just happens.
- Transformed takes time and effort.

WHAT HAPPENS IF YOU PUT ON THE _____ BEFORE TAKING OFF THE _____?

The new peels off.

- Renewal takes time.
- Time is your friend.

_____ AND _____

ARE NOT ENOUGH.

If you think the way you used to think, you'll do the things you used to do.

SEVEN LETHAL _____:

"If I can find the right person, everything will be all right."

"My situation is unique."

"It's not right, but it makes me happy. God wants me to be happy."

"If only I had _____, then I would be satisfied."

"I owe" is better than "I want."

"My secret is safe with me."

"Sex will solve it."

CONCLUSION

It's not enough to *ask* the question: "What was I thinking?" You have to *answer* it. That way, next time will look much different than last time.

Next time can be better than last time through the renewing of your mind.

POST A
PICTURE OF
YOUR GROUP USING
#StartingOverSeries.

Your next study could be on us!

Answer Key for Blanks		
transformed	old	resolve
new	regret	assumptions

Notes

LET'S TALK ABOUT IT

1 Did you hear anything in the video that you disagreed with or that stands out to you?

2 Do you have a personal example of when time allowed you to renew your mind?

3 Andy addressed seven statements and labeled them "lethal assumptions." Discuss situations when people justify their behavior with these assumptions.

"If I can find the right person, everything will be all right."

"My situation is unique."

"It's not right, but it makes me happy. God wants me to be happy."

"If only I had _____, then I would be satisfied."

"I owe" is better than "I want."

"My secret is safe with me."

"Sex will solve it."

Notes

4 What might be the cost of a person still living with the mindset of these lethal assumptions instead of rethinking them?

5 Which of the seven assumptions is your most common excuse or justification for your actions?

THIS WEEK, THINK ABOUT...

1. Is there an area in your life where you would benefit from renewing your mind or changing the way you think?

2. Which of these practical methods for renewing your mind can you commit to do this week?

   ☐ Read Scripture.
   ☐ Attend church on Sunday.
   ☐ Meet with a mentor.
   ☐ Pray.
   ☐ Share your situation with a small group.
   ☐ Read a book about the topic.

PRAYER

God, help me realize the thought patterns that have led to past failures. Please give me the courage to think differently this week and in the days ahead.

IF YOU *continue* TO THINK THE WAY YOU USED *to think*, HISTORY WILL REPEAT *itself.*

PART 4
Release It

VIDEO RECAP

TWO KEY QUESTIONS:

1. How far into your _____ do you intend to carry the angst created in your _____?

2. How long do you plan to allow the people who mistreated you to influence you?

THEY DECIDED.

When you hear stories about people with shocking pasts who aren't living with anger and resentment, 100 percent of the time they decided: My past will remind me, not define me.

"I decided there was enough pain in life. I wasn't going to drag that along with me the rest of my life. It wasn't worth it."

TO BE SURE THAT _____ TIME IS BETTER THAN LAST TIME, _____ THE PAST SO THE PAST CAN *RELEASE* **YOU.**

Forgiveness allows you to carry the lessons of the past while leaving the baggage in the past.

"In your anger do not sin": Do not let the sun go down while you are still angry, and do not give the devil a foothold ... Get rid of all bitterness, rage and anger, brawling and slander, along with every form of malice. Be kind and compassionate to one another, forgiving each other, just as in Christ God forgave you.

(Ephesians 4:26–27, 31–32)

Video Notes

PARDON AS YOU HAVE BEEN _____.

- Go first so you can go on.
- Make a list of what they owe you.

CONCLUSION

Decide how far into your future you intend to carry the angst created in your past. If you release the past, the past can release you.

Answer Key for Blanks

future	next	pardoned
past	release	

POST A
PICTURE OF
YOUR GROUP USING
#StartingOverSeries.

Your next study could be on us!

25

LET'S TALK ABOUT IT

1 In the message, Andy gave an example of a friend who lives with such peace that you would never guess her past is so complicated. Do you know anyone like this?

2 Talk about a time when you decided to forgive someone. Did the decision affect how you thought or felt toward that person?

3 Below is a list of some areas in which people commonly believe they are owed. Check off the "costs" from the list that resonate with you.

You cost me my...

☐ Ability to have children
☐ Best years
☐ Career
☐ Childhood
☐ Finances/money
☐ Future employment options
☐ Future plans
☐ Happy childhood
☐ Health
☐ Hope for a certain kind of father
☐ Hope for a certain kind of mother
☐ House
☐ Marriage
☐ Peace
☐ Plan for how things should have worked out
☐ Purity
☐ Relationships with my children
☐ Relationships with my friends
☐ Relationship with my parents
☐ Reputation
☐ Safety and security
☐ Success
☐ Time
☐ Other _____

More questions next page.

Notes

4 From the list on the previous page, which ones do you think people have the hardest time "releasing"?

5 If you feel comfortable, share a personal example from a box you checked.

6 Do you think it's possible to forgive someone without the other person seeking forgiveness from you first?

THIS WEEK, THINK ABOUT...

1. Have you carried any angst created in your past into your present? Which relationship(s) in your life is being affected?

2. What is your plan to begin forgiving the person who has wronged you?

Notes

PRAYER

God, help me have the courage to forgive those who caused pain in my past. I want my future to be free of the angst that I've been carrying.

DECIDE HOW far into your *future* YOU INTEND TO *carry* the ANGST created IN YOUR *past.*

POST A
PICTURE OF
YOUR GROUP USING
#StartingOverSeries.

Your next study could be on us!

Notes